Reading Essentials®
in Science

TEACHING AND ASSESSMENT RESOURCE

DOWN TO EARTH!

PERFECTION LEARNING®

Editorial Director: Susan C. Thies
Editor: Mary L. Bush
Writer: Traci Pedersen

Design Director: Randy Messer
Cover Design: Michael A. Aspengren
Book Design: Deborah Lea Bell, Emily J. Greazel, Carol M. Berg

Image Credits:
Corbis (Royalty-Free): p. 11; Emily Greazel: p. 57; Ingram: p. 22; MapArt: pp. 44, 65, 67, 71, 75; Perfection Learning Corporation: p. 29; Photos.com: pp. 5, 6, 13, 23, 24, 25, 26, 30, 34, 40, 41, 45, 48, 51, 54, 55, 59, 68, 70, 72; Sue Cornelison: p. 53

For information, contact
Perfection Learning® Corporation
1000 North Second Avenue, P.O. Box 500
Logan, Iowa 51546-0500.
Phone: 1-800-831-4190 • Fax: 1-800-543-2745
perfectionlearning.com
Printed in the United States of America

1 2 3 4 5 PP 10 09 08 07 06

ISBN 0-7891-6648-8

Table of Contents

continued

Table of Contents *continued*

Reading Essentials® in Science

> " 'Begin at the beginning,' the king said gravely,
> 'and go till you come to the end; then stop.' "
> Lewis Carroll,
> *Alice's Adventures in Wonderland*, (1865), p. 12

Unfortunately, this is the way many learners read—from beginning to end—regardless of the reading task in front of them, whether it be reading for information or pleasure, expository or narrative. This passive, linear approach to text compromises understanding and reading success. Successful readers need to be actively involved in the reading process, monitoring their understanding, personally relating to the text, and applying what they know to understand what they're reading.

While active reading strategies are important to the comprehension of any type of reading material, they are especially important in understanding informational, or expository, text. It is estimated that about 90 percent of adult reading is to acquire information, while only about 10 percent is for pleasure. So content literacy skills will be important to students far beyond their school years. In their interactions with informational text, student readers should be learning content while developing the literacy and thinking skills necessary to become lifelong readers.

Reading Essentials in Science helps readers learn more about concepts introduced in science and develop content literacy strategies. Few students ever develop a passion for reading from their science textbooks. The interesting, visually appealing, reader-friendly student books in *Reading Essentials in Science* provide essential content and content-area reading practice as they pique students' interest. And the content literacy skills and strategies presented and practiced in the accompanying activities in the strand resources will prepare students for a lifetime of enjoyable and meaningful literacy experiences.

Overview of the Program

Reading Essentials in Science offers curricular-aligned informational books for students in grades 3 to 8, strand resources for practice and assessment of content and content literacy strategies, and a program resource for teaching content literacy strategies.

Reading Essentials in Science Student Books

The interesting and informative nonfiction titles are arranged in thematic strands with five related books per strand. The science strands are organized using the following disciplines: Earth/Space Science, Life Science, Physical Science, and Science in Social and Personal Perspectives.

Reading Essentials in Science Teaching and Assessment Resources

The reproducible strand resources offer students opportunities to extend content knowledge and develop and practice content literacy strategies. Additionally, objective tests are provided for each title to monitor student growth. These comprehensive resources have a separate section for each of the five titles in the strands.

Reading Essentials Content-Area Literacy Strategies Resource

This collection of research-based content literacy strategies will help you make the best use of the student books and the practice and assessment activities in the strand resource.

Features and Benefits of the *Reading Essentials in Science Teaching and Assessment Resources*

The following pages explain the features and benefits that are standard within the teacher information and student activities that comprise the Teaching and Assessment Resources.

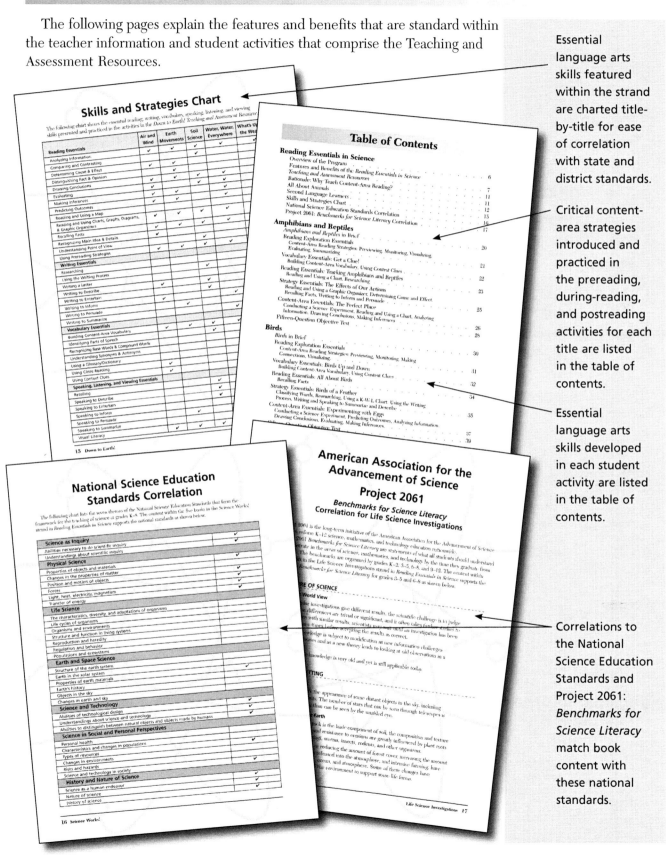

Essential language arts skills featured within the strand are charted title-by-title for ease of correlation with state and district standards.

Critical content-area strategies introduced and practiced in the prereading, during-reading, and postreading activities for each title are listed in the table of contents.

Essential language arts skills developed in each student activity are listed in the table of contents.

Correlations to the National Science Education Standards and Project 2061: *Benchmarks for Science Literacy* match book content with these national standards.

A detailed summary highlights the important science concepts covered in the book.

Vocabulary words that are boldfaced in the text and found in the book glossary are presented on the teacher page for reference.

Prereading, during-reading, and postreading activities suggested on the teacher page build background knowledge, activate prior knowledge, enhance comprehension, make connections, and extend content materials.

Essential content-area reading strategies introduced and practiced in the Reading Exploration activities are referenced in the footer.

Reading Essentials in Science

Acids and Bases
in Brief

A home tour reveals acids and bases found around the house. These substances are in foods, medicines, cleaning agents, and car batteries. While many are edible, others are poisonous or caustic.

When atoms combine to form compounds, they exchange or share electrons. This makes them charged atoms called *ions*. Acids and bases are compounds that either gain or lose a specific type of ion when they react with other substances.

An acid is a compound that releases hydrogen ions when dissolved in water. Acids have certain chemical properties. They taste sour and turn blue litmus paper red. They have the ability to conduct electricity when in solution, and they react with certain materials to form a gas. Acids are also corrosive. When an acid reacts with a base, the result is a salt and water. This is called *neutralization*.

A base is a compound that releases hydroxide ions or accepts free hydrogen ions in solution. Bases also have chemical properties that define them. They feel slippery to the touch. Bases taste bitter and turn red litmus paper blue. Like acids, bases can conduct electricity in solution. They also form a salt and water when reacting with an acid.

An indicator is used to determine whether a substance is an acid, a base, or neither. Indicators are materials that change different colors in the presence of an acid, base, or neutral substance. Litmus paper, bromothymol blue, and phenolphthalein are common indicators. Many plant and flower pigments are natural indicators.

Acids and bases vary in their strength. A high concentration of free hydrogen ions in a solution results in a stronger acid. Strong bases take up almost all of the hydrogen ions in a solution or have molecules that let go of hydroxide ions easily. The measure of the strength of an acid or base is called pH. Acids have a low pH, while bases have a high pH. The pH scale ranges from 0 to 14, with 7 being neutral. Each number on the scale is actually 10 times stronger or weaker than the one above or below it.

Acids and bases are at work in the ground, in the air, and in water. Acid rain eats away at rock and pollutes soil and groundwater. Fish tanks and swimming pools must maintain a healthy pH level. Acids such as DNA and hydrochloric acid play important roles in the human body. However, too much acid in a body can be harmful and must be balanced by a diet rich in basic foods. Acids and bases are also found in the products that people depend on every day.

Acids and Bases 20

The Heart

Reading Exploration Essentials

Vocabulary

artery	atrium	blood vessel	capillary
cell	coronary artery	heart attack	lung
muscle	nutrient	organ	pulse
septum	tissue	valve	vein
ventricle			

Reading Exploration

prereading

Use a K-W-L chart to introduce the heart. Distribute a chart to each student or guide students in creating their own chart. Ask them to fill in the "What I Know" column using their prior knowledge about the heart. Encourage students to share their ideas. Then ask them to fill in the "What I Want to Know" column.

What I Know	What I Want to Know	What I Learned

during reading

Help students cut a paper heart out of construction paper. Ask them to use the heart to take notes as they read *The Heart*. They can jot down main ideas, vocabulary words, and answers to their K-W-L questions. You can post the hearts on a bulletin board titled "Heartfelt Notes."

postreading

Have students fill out the "What I Learned" column of the K-W-L chart. Share ideas in small groups.

It's All the Same to the Fish

A *synonym* is a word that means the same or nearly the same as another word. For example, the statement "fish are water animals" means the same as "fish are water creatures." *Animals* and *creatures* are synonyms.

Read each sentence below. Find the synonym of the italicized word(s). Write the word on the line.

camouflage	dams	habitats	mates
membrane	organisms	predators	prey
scales	species		

_____ 1. More than 25,000 different *types* of fish make their home underwater.

_____ 2. A covering of tough *plates* protects most fish from harm.

_____ 3. A fin is made of a thin *tissue* stretched over rods called spines.

_____ 4. A shark's strong sense of smell leads it to *victims*.

_____ 5. Tartan hawkfish are one kind of fish that use *protective coloring* to stay hidden among plants in the water.

_____ 6. Eels are covered with a slippery slime that makes it hard for *hunters* to catch them.

_____ 7. Plankton are tiny *living things* that fish eat.

_____ 8. Fish ladders help salmon find a way around *barriers*.

_____ 9. Bioluminescence helps fish find food and *partners*.

_____ 10. Water pollution threatens fish *homes*.

● **One Step Further:** An *antonym* is a word that means the opposite of another word. Which of the two vocabulary words above are antonyms?

Flat or Round?

The Earth

It took thousands of years to prove that the Earth wasn't flat. During that time, many people held the opinion that it was silly to believe that the Earth was round. Only a few men, such as Aristotle and Christopher Columbus, disagreed. Today, however, we know that it's a fact that the Earth is round. Space travel has proven it to be true.

Read the following statements. Decide whether each one is a fact (something proven) or an opinion (something believed by someone). Write F for fact or O for opinion.

_____ 1. The Sun is a star.

_____ 2. Space travel is an exciting career.

_____ 3. Earth is the most important planet in the Solar System.

_____ 4. The Earth is tilted on an axis.

_____ 5. Astronomy is an interesting hobby.

_____ 6. Galileo was the first scientist to use a telescope to look at the sky.

_____ 7. It was wrong for the church to forbid Galileo to leave his house because he believed the Earth revolved around the Sun.

_____ 8. The Earth's path around the Sun is an ellipse.

_____ 9. The Earth's rotation causes day and night.

_____ 10. It would be best to live by the equator where the seasons don't change.

● **One Step Further:** Find out more facts about one of the scientists or explorers who was important in discovering the Earth's properties. Choose from Sir Isaac Newton, Nicolaus Copernicus, Galileo Galilei, Christopher Columbus, or Aristotle. Write a short report on one of these men. Describe their accomplishments. Include at least one opinion about the man or his work. Share your report with classmates.

Each title-specific section offers a Vocabulary Essentials activity to build content-area vocabulary.

One Step Further suggestions provide skills application and extension.

A Reading Essentials activity for each title develops critical literacy skills.

Low-stakes writing is integrated into at least one student activity per title.

Essential language arts skills presented and practiced in the student activities are referenced in the footer.

A Strategy Essentials activity for each title utilizes specific strategies to help students master the content and monitor their own learning. The content-area strategies practiced are prominently displayed in the header.

A Content-Area Essentials activity for each title investigates science concepts and reinforces scientific language and procedure through experiments and hands-on activities.

Many of the experiments include a "Stop and Predict" or "Form a Hypothesis" section for experience predicting scientific outcomes.

A Fifteen-Question Objective Test assesses student learning using a format similar to most state and national tests.

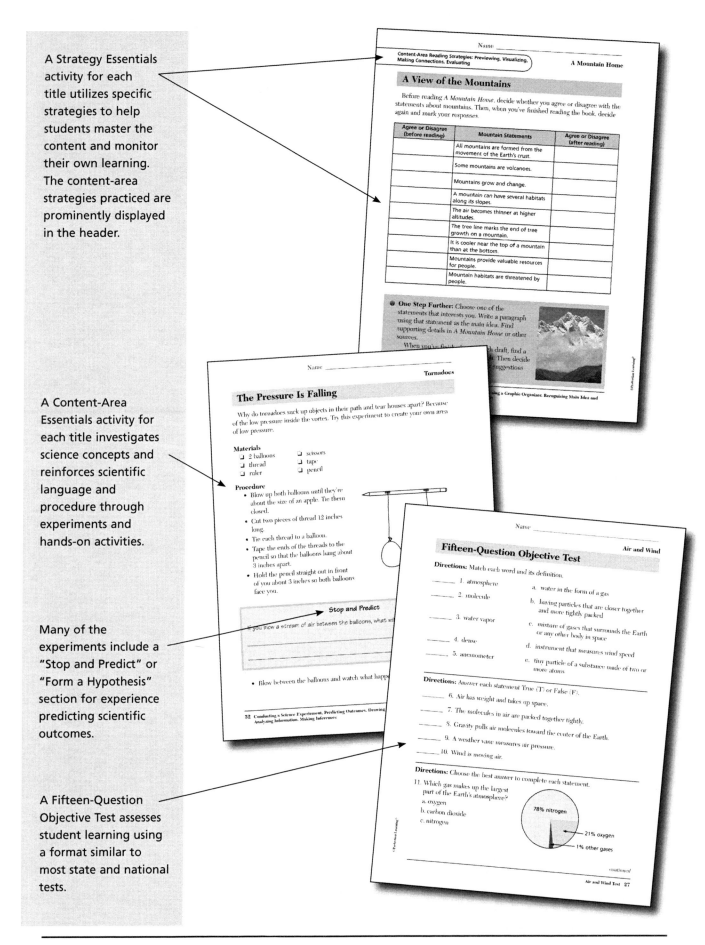

Name _____

Content-Area Reading Strategies: Previewing, Visualizing, Making Connections, Evaluating

A Mountain Home

A View of the Mountains

Before reading *A Mountain Home*, decide whether you agree or disagree with the statements about mountains. Then, when you've finished reading the book, decide again and mark your responses.

Agree or Disagree (before reading)	Mountain Statements	Agree or Disagree (after reading)
	All mountains are formed from the movement of the Earth's crust.	
	Some mountains are volcanoes.	
	Mountains grow and change.	
	A mountain can have several habitats along its slopes.	
	The air becomes thinner at higher altitudes.	
	The tree line marks the end of tree growth on a mountain.	
	It is cooler near the top of a mountain than at the bottom.	
	Mountains provide valuable resources for people.	
	Mountain habitats are threatened by people.	

● **One Step Further:** Choose one of the statements that interests you. Write a paragraph using that statement as the main idea. Find supporting details in *A Mountain Home* or other sources.

When you've finished your first draft, find a partner to read your paragraph. Then decide suggestions.

Using a Graphic Organizer, Recognizing Main Idea and

Name _____

Tornadoes

The Pressure Is Falling

Why do tornadoes suck up objects in their path and tear houses apart? Because of the low pressure inside the vortex. Try this experiment to create your own area of low pressure.

Materials
- 2 balloons
- thread
- ruler
- scissors
- tape
- pencil

Procedure
- Blow up both balloons until they're about the size of an apple. Tie them closed.
- Cut two pieces of thread 12 inches long.
- Tie each thread to a balloon.
- Tape the ends of the threads to the pencil so that the balloons hang about 3 inches apart.
- Hold the pencil straight out in front of you about 3 inches so both balloons face you.

Stop and Predict

If you blow a stream of air between the balloons, what wil

- Blow between the balloons and watch what happ

52 Conducting a Science Experiment, Predicting Outcomes, Drawing Analyzing Information, Making Inferences

Name _____

Air and Wind

Fifteen-Question Objective Test

Directions: Match each word and its definition.

_____ 1. atmosphere

_____ 2. molecule

_____ 3. water vapor

_____ 4. dense

_____ 5. anemometer

a. water in the form of a gas

b. having particles that are closer together and more tightly packed

c. mixture of gases that surrounds the Earth or any other body in space

d. instrument that measures wind speed

e. tiny particle of a substance made of two or more atoms

Directions: Answer each statement True (T) or False (F).

_____ 6. Air has weight and takes up space.

_____ 7. The molecules in air are packed together tightly.

_____ 8. Gravity pulls air molecules toward the center of the Earth.

_____ 9. A weather vane measures air pressure.

_____ 10. Wind is moving air.

Directions: Choose the best answer to complete each statement.

11. Which gas makes up the largest part of the Earth's atmosphere?
   a. oxygen
   b. carbon dioxide
   c. nitrogen

78% nitrogen
21% oxygen
1% other gases

continued

Air and Wind Test 27

Rationale: Why Teach Content-Area Reading?

Many mistakenly believe that students do not need further reading instruction once they learn to decode. However, reading goes beyond mere decoding. Content comprehension is dependent upon an active relationship between the reader and the text. Teaching reading in the content areas helps learners make connections between what they know and the new information in the text.

In order to develop content-area knowledge, students need interesting, relevant content-area books. Additionally, students need to develop and practice content-area strategies to learn to interact with the text and create meaning. Many readers have never been taught that they need to think when they are reading and to create pictures in their mind. Reading is not passive word calling. Readers who are not actively involved in their reading, who aren't monitoring their understanding by personally relating to the text and applying what they know to understand what they're reading, will finish with little or no understanding of what they've read. Often they lose confidence in themselves as readers, give up on reading, and fall behind.

The science titles and content-area literacy skills and strategies presented and practiced in the *Reading Essentials in Science* program will help students learn *how* to learn, enabling them to acquire knowledge independently from their reading in school and throughout their lives.

Down to Earth!

Down to Earth! Student Books

The five titles in the Down to Earth! series are *Air and Wind*; *Earth Movements*; *Soil Science*; *Water, Water, Everywhere*; and *What's Up with the Weather? A Look at Climate*. Each title offers information about the basic materials and forces that shape life on Earth. Each title features an index and a glossary. The content-specific vocabulary included in the glossary is bolded throughout the text. Additionally, Internet sites and related books are provided to extend the information presented.

The Reading Essentials in Science Down to Earth! titles contain considerate text that is well organized and clearly written. In this way, readers are actively involved in their learning as they make connections and create meaning.

Down to Earth! Teaching and Assessment Resource

This comprehensive resource covers all five titles in the strand. Each title-specific section offers

- a synopsis of the chapters in the student book

- reading exploration activities (prereading, during reading, and postreading)
  In order for students to understand the new information presented in the books, they need to relate what they're reading to what they already know. The prereading activities help learners call up prior knowledge and make connections to what they're learning. The during-reading and postreading suggestions provide students with a purpose for reading and guide them in using active reading strategies.

- a content-specific vocabulary activity
  Research shows that vocabulary knowledge is one of the most important factors in increased comprehension.

- a reading skills activity
  Reading skills activities link essential reading skills and strategies with important content.

- a content literacy strategy activity
  Students need to learn and practice specific content literacy strategies, in other words, how to be actively involved in their reading.

- a hands-on activity
  As students complete hands-on activities related to the content, they extend their subject matter knowledge.

- an objective test
  Objective assessment is presented in a format similar to the questions on state and standardized tests.

In addition, a writing activity is incorporated into at least one of the activities above. This gives students the opportunity to practice writing skills and make personal connections between the content and themselves.

Second Language Learners

The terms English for Speakers of Other Languages (ESOL), English as a Second Language (ESL), and English Language Learners (ELL) were developed to recognize students whose heritage language is other than English. Classrooms today are comprised of a rich variety of heritages and languages reflecting the diverse cultural nature of our society. The Limited English Proficiency (LEP) students enter the classroom at various limited English language levels. They are faced with challenging content in an unfamiliar language. An appropriate instructional model must be in place for these students. ESOL instruction is designed to meet the needs of LEP students by providing instruction based on their level of English proficiency.

When developing and enriching instruction through ESOL strategies, the educator must be sensitive to the student's first language and cultural background while at the same time encouraging the student to acquire the English language in a nonthreatening and productive learning environment. The student's individual differences and learning styles must also be considered when applying ESOL strategies. All LEP students are entitled to equal educational opportunities that include access to materials, programs, and experiences.

Using *Reading Essentials in Science* with Limited English Students

The *Reading Essentials in Science* program offers LEP students an opportunity to learn grade-level content as they acquire proficiency in the English language. Through the use of certain instructional strategies, LEP students, representing a diverse group of language backgrounds and individual differences, can find success with the same books that are being enjoyed by their English-speaking classmates.

The use of graphic organizers is an effective ESOL strategy. Flow charts, pie charts, family trees, Venn diagrams, etc., are all appropriate and recommended. Additionally, cooperative learning groups offer support and nonthreatening learning environments for LEP students as they develop linguistic and academic skills.

The additional strategies shown below should be used at certain times throughout the lesson to help each student's individual language development and to help him or her progress to a proficient English language level.

Before Reading

Content-area vocabulary is provided on the inside front covers of all *Reading Essentials in Science* titles. While all students benefit from the preteaching of content vocabulary, it is critical for LEP students. They cannot rely on context clues and general background knowledge to the extent their English-language peers can. Introduce the vocabulary in context and use picture cues with vocabulary definitions to ensure understanding.

Below are some specific strategies that will better prepare LEP students to access the core content information in *Reading Essentials in Science*.

- Encourage communication in the classroom setting. LEP students learn so much by listening to their peers.

- Develop predictions based on cover art and book titles. Many of the *Reading Essentials in Science* books include images that are recognizable to English-speaking students but won't be to LEP students. Make sure images and their relationship to the content are clearly explained.

- Use graphic organizers. Build webs around content vocabulary introduced to expand language acquisition and deepen understanding.

- Make the language comprehensible through the use of gestures, visuals, concrete examples, and oral communication.

- Use the suggested activities in this teacher resource to build background knowledge. Restate, expand, paraphrase, repeat, and speak clearly and slowly.

During Reading

The *Reading Essentials in Science* books are filled with colorful, descriptive visuals. Use the graphics to create meaning for your students. Study and discuss the visuals as well as the text.

Additionally, the following specific strategies will help LEP students acquire the core knowledge presented in the *Reading Essentials in Science* books.

- Continuously refer to the vocabulary in context.

- Draw on students' personal experiences to add meaning to the discussion.

- Provide for much discussion and encourage students to contribute through their thoughts, questions, and opinions.

- Allow oral and written responses to accommodate individual differences.

- Provide time for directed dialogue between student pairs and between teacher and student.

- Encourage journal writing: reflective, descriptive, and expository.

- Tape selections for students.

- Allow for an extended response time. LEP students need time to process their thoughts and responses in an unfamiliar language.

After Reading

In addition to the reading, writing, and content-area activities provided in this resource, use the following strategies with your LEP students to extend and assess the content information presented.

- Encourage students to express personal reactions through written, oral, or pictorial activities.

- Arrange students in cooperative groups to complete the reading and content-area activities.

- Offer students a chance to complete the objective test orally rather than in writing.

Skills and Strategies Chart

The following chart shows the essential reading, writing, vocabulary, speaking, listening, and viewing skills presented and practiced in the activities in the *Down to Earth! Teaching and Assessment Resource.*

Reading Essentials	Air and Wind	Earth Movements	Soil Science	Water, Water, Everywhere	What's Up with the Weather?
Analyzing Information	✔	✔	✔	✔	✔
Comparing and Contrasting			✔		
Determining Cause & Effect	✔	✔			
Distinguishing Fact & Opinion		✔			
Drawing Conclusions	✔	✔	✔	✔	✔
Evaluating	✔	✔	✔	✔	
Making Inferences	✔	✔		✔	
Predicting Outcomes	✔	✔		✔	
Reading and Using a Map					✔
Reading and Using Charts, Graphs, Diagrams, & Graphic Organizers	✔	✔	✔	✔	
Recalling Facts	✔	✔	✔	✔	✔
Recognizing Main Idea & Details	✔				
Understanding Point of View			✔		
Using Prereading Strategies	✔	✔	✔	✔	✔
Writing Essentials					
Researching					
Using the Writing Process			✔		
Writing a Letter					✔
Writing to Describe	✔		✔		
Writing to Entertain			✔		
Writing to Inform	✔			✔	✔
Writing to Persuade		✔			✔
Writing to Summarize				✔	
Vocabulary Essentials					
Building Content-Area Vocabulary	✔	✔	✔	✔	✔
Identifying Parts of Speech			✔		
Recognizing Base Words & Compound Words				✔	
Understanding Synonyms & Antonyms					✔
Using a Glossary/Dictionary				✔	
Using Cloze Reading	✔				
Using Context Clues	✔				
Speaking, Listening, and Viewing Essentials					
Retelling			✔		
Speaking to Describe			✔		
Speaking to Entertain			✔		
Speaking to Inform				✔	
Speaking to Persuade		✔			
Speaking to Summarize				✔	
Visual Literacy	✔	✔	✔	✔	✔

National Science Education Standards Correlation

The following chart lists the seven themes of the National Science Education Standards that form the framework for the teaching of science at grades K–8. The content within the five books in the Down to Earth! strand in *Reading Essentials in Science* supports the national standards as shown below.

Science as Inquiry	
Abilities necessary to do scientific inquiry	✔
Understandings about scientific inquiry	✔
Physical Science	
Properties of objects and materials	✔
Changes in the properties of matter	✔
Position and motion of objects	✔
Forces	✔
Light, heat, electricity, magnetism	
Transfer of energy	✔
Life Science	
The characteristics, diversity, and adaptations of organisms	
Life cycles of organisms	
Organisms and environments	✔
Structure and function in living systems	
Reproduction and heredity	
Regulation and behavior	
Populations and ecosystems	
Earth and Space Science	
Structure of the earth system	✔
Earth in the solar system	✔
Properties of earth materials	✔
Earth's history	✔
Objects in the sky	
Changes in earth and sky	✔
Science and Technology	
Abilities of technological design	✔
Understandings about science and technology	✔
Abilities to distinguish between natural objects and objects made by humans	✔
Science in Social and Personal Perspectives	
Personal health	
Characteristics and changes in populations	
Types of resources	✔
Changes in environments	✔
Risks and hazards	
Science and technology in society	✔
History and Nature of Science	
Science as a human endeavor	✔
Nature of science	✔
History of science	✔

American Association for the Advancement of Science

Project 2061

Benchmarks for Science Literacy
Correlation for Down to Earth!

Project 2061 is the long-term initiative of the American Association for the Advancement of Science working to reform K–12 science, mathematics, and technology education nationwide.

Project 2061: *Benchmarks for Science Literacy* are statements of what all students should understand and demonstrate in the areas of science, mathematics, and technology by the time they graduate from high school. The benchmarks are organized by grades K–2, 3–5, 6–8, and 9–12. The content within the five books in the Down to Earth! strand in *Reading Essentials in Science* supports the Project 2061: *Benchmarks for Science Literacy* for grades 3–5 and 6–8 as shown below.

THE NATURE OF SCIENCE

The Scientific World View

- When similar investigations give different results, the scientific challenge is to judge whether the differences are trivial or significant, and it often takes further studies to decide. Even with similar results, scientists may wait until an investigation has been repeated many times before accepting the results as correct.

- Scientific knowledge is subject to modification as new information challenges prevailing theories and as a new theory leads to looking at old observations in a new way.

- Some scientific knowledge is very old and yet is still applicable today.

THE PHYSICAL SETTING

The Universe

- The earth is one of several planets that orbit the sun, and the moon orbits around the earth.

The Earth

- Things on or near the earth are pulled toward it by the earth's gravity.

- Like all planets and stars, the earth is approximately spherical in shape. The rotation of the earth on its axis every 24 hours produces the night-and-day cycle. To people on earth, this turning of the planet makes it seem as though the sun, moon, planets, and stars are orbiting the earth once a day.

- When liquid water disappears, it turns into a gas (vapor) in the air and can reappear as a liquid when cooled or as a solid if cooled below the freezing point of water. Clouds and fog are made of tiny droplets of water.

- Air is a substance that surrounds us, takes up space, and whose movement we feel as wind.

- The earth is mostly rock. Three-fourths of its surface is covered by a relatively thick layer of water (some of it frozen), and the entire planet is surrounded by a relatively thin blanket of air. It is the only body in the solar system that appears able to support life. The other planets have compositions and conditions very different from the earth's.
- Everything on or anywhere near the earth is pulled toward the earth's center by gravitational force.
- Because the earth turns daily on an axis that is tilted relative to the plane of the earth's yearly orbit around the sun, sunlight falls more intensely on different parts of the earth during the year. The difference in the heating of the earth's surface produces the planet's seasons and weather patterns.
- Climates have sometimes changed abruptly in the past as a result of changes in the earth's crust, such as volcanic eruptions or impacts of huge rocks from space. Even relatively small changes in atmospheric or ocean content can have widespread effects on climate if the change lasts long enough.
- The cycling of water in and out of the atmosphere plays an important role in determining climatic patters. Water evaporates from the surface of the earth, rises and cools, condenses into rain or snow, and falls again to the surface. The water falling on land collects in rivers and lakes, soil, and porous layers of rock, and much of it flows back into the ocean.
- Fresh water, limited in supply, is essential for life and also for most industrial processes. Rivers, lakes, and groundwater can be depleted or polluted, becoming unavailable or unsuitable for life.
- Heat energy carried by ocean currents has a strong influence on climate around the world.
- The benefits of the earth's resources—such as fresh water, air, soil, and trees—can be reduced by using them wastefully or by deliberately or inadvertently destroying them. The atmosphere and the oceans have a limited capacity to absorb wastes and recycle materials naturally. Cleaning up polluted air, water, or soil or restoring depleted soil, forests, or fishing grounds can be very difficult and costly.

Processes That Shape the Earth
- Waves, wind, water and ice shape and reshape the earth's land surface by eroding rock and soil in some areas and depositing them in other areas, sometimes in seasonal layers.
- Rock is composed of different combinations of minerals. Smaller rocks come from the breakage and weathering of bedrock and larger rocks. Soil is made partly from weathered rock, partly from plant remains—and also contains many living organisms.
- The interior of the earth is hot. Heat flow and movement of material within the earth cause earthquakes and volcanic eruptions and create mountains and ocean basins. Gas and dust from large volcanoes can change the atmosphere.
- Some changes in the earth's surface are abrupt (such as earthquakes and volcanic eruptions) while other changes happen very slowly (such as uplift and wearing down of mountains). The earth's surface is shaped in part by the motion of water and wind over very long times, which act to level mountain ranges.
- Sediments of sand and smaller particles (sometimes containing the remains of organisms) are gradually buried and are cemented together by dissolved minerals to form solid rock again.

- Sedimentary rock buried deep enough may be reformed by pressure and heat, perhaps melting and recrystallizing into different kinds of rock. These re-formed rock layers may be forced up again to become land surface and even mountains. Subsequently, this new rock too will erode. Rock bears evidence of the minerals, temperatures, and forces that created it.

- Although weathered rock is the basic component of soil, the composition and texture of soil and its fertility and resistance to erosions are greatly influenced by plant roots and debris, bacteria, fungi, worms, insects, rodents, and other organisms.

- Human activities, such as reducing the amount of forest cover, increasing the amount and variety of chemicals released into the atmosphere, and intensive farming, have changed the earth's land, ocean, and atmosphere. Some of these changes have decreased the capacity of the environment to support some life forms.

The Structure of Matter

- Heating and cooling cause changes in the properties of materials. Many kinds of changes occur faster under hotter conditions.

- Materials may be composed of parts that are too small to be seen without magnification.

- All matter is made up of atoms, which are far too small to see directly through a microscope. The atoms of any element are alike but are different from atoms of other elements. Atoms may stick together in well-defined molecules or may be packed together in large arrays. Different arrangements of atoms into groups compose all substances.

- Equal volumes of different substances usually have different weights.

- Atoms and molecules are perpetually in motion. Increased temperatures mean greater average energy, so most substances expand when heated. In solids, the atoms are closely locked in position and can only vibrate. In liquids, the atoms or molecules have higher energy, are more loosely connected, and can slide past one another; some molecules may get enough energy to escape into a gas. In gases, the atoms or molecules have still more energy and are free of one another except during occasional collisions.

Energy Transformations

- Most of what goes on in the universe—from exploding stars and biological growth to the operation of machines and the motion of people—involves some form of energy being transformed into another. Energy in the form of heat is almost always one of the products of an energy transformation.

Forces of Nature

- The earth's gravity pulls any object toward it without touching it.

THE HUMAN ORGANISM

Physical Health

- The environment may contain dangerous levels of substances that are harmful to human beings. Therefore, the good health of individuals requires monitoring the soil, air, and water and taking steps to keep them safe.

Technology and Science

- Throughout all of history, people everywhere have invented and used tools. Most tools of today are different from those of the past, but many are modifications of very ancient tools.

- Technology enables scientists and others to observe things that are too small or too far away to be seen without it and to study the motion of objects that are moving very rapidly or are hardly moving at all.

- Measuring instruments can be used to gather accurate information for making scientific comparisons of objects and events and for designing and constructing things that will work properly.

- Technology extends the ability of people to change the world: to cut, shape, or put together materials; to move things from one place to another; and to reach farther with their hands, voices, senses, and minds. The changes may be for survival needs such as food, shelter, and defense; for communication and transportation; or to gain knowledge and express ideas.

- Technology is essential to science for such purposes as access to outer space and other remote locations, sample collection and treatment, measurement, data collection and storage, computation, and communication of information.

Design and Systems

- The solution to one problem may create other problems.

Issues in Technology

- Technology has been part of life on the earth since the advent of the human species. Like language, ritual, commerce, and the arts, technology is an intrinsic part of human culture, and it both shapes society and is shaped by it. The technology available to people greatly influences what their lives are like.

- An invention is likely to lead to other inventions. Once an invention exists, people are likely to think of ways of using it that were never imagined at first.

- Because of their ability to invent tools and processes, people have an enormous effect on the lives of other living things.

- The human ability to shape the future comes from a capacity for generating knowledge and developing new technologies—and for communicating ideas to others.

- Technology cannot always provide successful solutions for problems or fulfill every human need.

- Technology has strongly influenced the course of history and continues to do so. It is largely responsible for the great revolutions in agriculture, manufacturing, sanitation and medicine, warfare, transportation, information processing, and communications that have radically changed how people live.

- New technologies increase some risks and decrease others. Some of the same technologies that have improved the length and quality of life for many people have also brought new risks.

- Societies influence what aspects of technology are developed and how these are used. People control technology (as well as science) and are responsible for its effects.

THE DESIGNED WORLD

Agriculture

- Some plant varieties and animal breeds have more desirable characteristics than others, but some may be more difficult or costly to grow. The kinds of crops that can grow in an area depend on the climate and soil. Irrigation and fertilizers can help crops grow in places where there is too little water or the soil is poor.

- Modern technology has increased the efficiency of agriculture so that fewer people are needed to work on farms than ever before.

- In agriculture, as in all technologies, there are always trade-offs to be made. Getting food from many different places makes people less dependent on weather in any one place, yet more dependent on transportation and communication among far-flung markets. Specializing in one crop may risk disaster if changes in weather or increases in pest populations wipe out that crop. Also, the soil may be exhausted of some nutrients, which can be replenished by rotating the right crops.

Energy Sources and Use

- Moving air and water can be used to run machines.

- Some energy sources cost less than others and some cause less pollution that others.

- Different ways of obtaining, transforming, and distributing energy have different environmental consequences.

- Electrical energy can be produced from a variety of energy sources and can be transformed into almost any other form of energy. Moreover, electricity is used to distribute energy quickly and conveniently to distant locations.

Health Technology

- Sanitation measures such as the use of sewers, landfills, quarantines, and safe food handling are important in controlling the spread of organisms that cause disease. Improving sanitation to prevent disease has contributed more to saving human life than any advance in medical treatment.

COMMON THEMES

Models

- Models are often used to think about processes that happen too slowly, too quickly, or on too small a scale to observe directly, or that are too vast to be changed deliberately, or that are potentially dangerous.

Air and Wind
in Brief

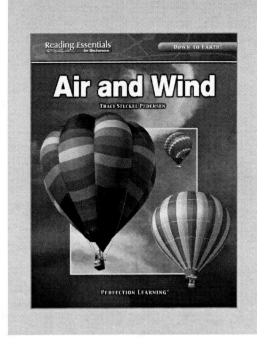

People living in ancient times had many questions about the mysterious substance that seemed to surround them. It took thousands of years and many scientific experiments to understand how air affects our lives. Today we recognize that air fuels our bodies, produces weather, and creates electricity.

Air has several unique properties that determine its behavior and importance. Air is a gas made up of 78 percent nitrogen and 21 percent oxygen. The last 1 percent is a mixture of other gases such as carbon dioxide, argon, hydrogen, and helium. Even though its molecules are invisible, air still takes up space like all other materials. Under normal conditions, air is not a dense substance because its molecules are spread far apart. Hot air rises, while cold air sinks. Because air contains fewer molecules in a given space, it is extremely light compared to liquids and solids. This is why air "floats" above the Earth's surface. Gravity pulls air molecules toward the center of the Earth, creating air pressure. Air pressure changes with density.

The atmosphere is a blanket of air surrounding the Earth. The atmosphere is divided into five layers—the troposphere, stratosphere, mesosphere, thermosphere, and exosphere. The troposphere is the part of the atmosphere that we breathe. It is where most weather develops. The stratosphere contains the ozone layer that absorbs and scatters the Sun's powerful ultraviolet rays. The mesosphere is a cold layer that stretches from 31 to 50 miles above the Earth's surface. In the thermosphere, radio waves bounce off energy particles and carry broadcasts from all over the world. The exosphere is the outer layer of the atmosphere that merges into outer space.

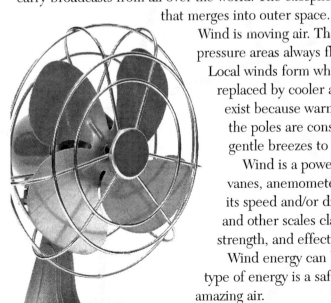

Wind is moving air. The movement occurs because air in high-pressure areas always flows toward areas of lower pressure. Local winds form when warm air over land rises and is replaced by cooler air from over nearby water. Global winds exist because warm air from the equator and cold air from the poles are constantly moving. Wind speeds vary from gentle breezes to violent tornado and hurricane winds.

Wind is a powerful force. Instruments such as weather vanes, anemometers, and aerovanes are used to measure its speed and/or direction. The Beaufort Wind Scale and other scales classify winds according to their speed, strength, and effects.

Wind energy can be used to create electrical power. This type of energy is a safe, clean way to make the most of our amazing air.

Reading Exploration Essentials

Vocabulary

aerovane	anemometer	atmosphere	atom
barometer	dense	exosphere	global
gravity	local	mesosphere	molecule
ozone layer	satellite	stratosphere	thermosphere
troposphere	water vapor	weather vane	

Reading Exploration

prereading

Write the following words on the board or overhead: *balloons, sailboats, kites, airplanes, weather vanes, flags, fans,* and *lungs.* Lead students in a think-pair-share discussion. Ask students to look at the words and think about what they have in common. Then pair students to share their ideas. Encourage pairs to share with the whole class. Guide students to arrive at the concept of things associated with air and/or wind.

during reading

As students read *Air and Wind*, ask them to keep a journal of words to add to the prereading list. For example, after Chapter 1, students might suggest words such as *nitrogen, oxygen, molecules, air pressure,* etc.

postreading

Have students work in small groups to share their word journals. Then ask each group to choose a speaker to share words. Go around the groups in a round-robin fashion with each group adding a new word until all words have been shared.

Ask each student to choose one of the words. Instruct students to draw a picture of the word and write a sentence or two explaining how the word relates to air or wind.

Windy Words

The wind has blown the vocabulary words out of the paragraphs below. Put the words back where they belong. Write them in the correct spaces. You won't use all of the words.

aerovane	dense	mesosphere	thermosphere
anemometer	exosphere	molecules	troposphere
atmosphere	global	ozone layer	water vapor
atom	gravity	satellites	weather vane
barometer	local	stratosphere	

The Earth's (1) _____ is divided

into five layers. The (2) _____ is

the bottom layer of the atmosphere. It extends

upward from the Earth's surface about 5 to

10 miles. It is the part of the atmosphere where

(3) _____ condenses into clouds.

Local and (4) _____ winds also

form in the troposphere.

The middle atmosphere begins in the (5) _____. This layer is

very important because it contains the (6) _____. This zone acts

as a protective sponge that absorbs and scatters the Sun's ultraviolet rays.

The (7) _____ is the other layer in the middle atmosphere.

Here temperatures begin to drop again. Temperatures can reach as low as -130°F.

The (8) _____ is named for its hot temperatures. The Sun's rays

cause the temperatures here to reach up to 2700°F! This layer is the beginning of

the upper atmosphere.

_____ *continued*

Windy Words *continued*

The outer layer of the atmosphere is the

(9) _____. The air here is less

(10) _____ than in any other layer.

It contains only tiny amounts of hydrogen and helium.

Many of the gas (11) _____ in this

layer escape (12) _____ and fly

into outer space. This layer is where

(13) _____ and space shuttles travel.

◎ **One Step Further:** Four of the remaining words are weather tools. Write a paragraph about these tools. Leave blank spaces where the vocabulary words should go. Exchange your paragraph with a partner. Can he or she fill in the blanks correctly?

_____

_____

_____

_____

_____

_____

_____

_____

Get the Idea?

Air and Wind explained many ideas about air and its movement. Read the paragraphs below. Underline the main idea sentence. Remember, the main idea tells what the entire paragraph is about.

1.   Hot-air balloons work using the movement of hot and cold air. When heated, the air inside a balloon becomes less dense than the air outside the balloon. This causes the balloon to rise. To land the balloon, a vent is opened so some of the hot air can escape. The cooler air now sinks, bringing the balloon down with it.

2.   As the Sun heats up the Earth's surface, the surface warms the air above it. This warm air then rises into the atmosphere. This creates an area of low pressure below. Cooler air then rushes in to fill up the "empty" space, creating wind. Eventually this air warms up and moves out, and the cycle continues. The Sun and air are perfect partners in the creation of wind.

3.   Several scales are used to classify winds. The Beaufort Wind Scale includes all winds from the lightest breeze to the strongest hurricane wind. The Saffir-Simpson Scale rates hurricane winds. The Fujita Pearson Tornado Damage Scale puts tornadoes into five categories based on their wind speeds.

continued

©Perfection Learning®

Get the Idea? *continued*

Now you try it. Below is a paragraph about air and wind. The paragraph is missing a main idea sentence. Read the supporting details. Then write a main idea sentence on the lines.

4. _____

_____.

A barometer measures air pressure. A weather vane shows which direction the wind is coming from. An anemometer records wind speed. An aerovane is a combination of a weather vane and an anemometer. It measures both wind speed and direction.

Now that you understand main idea, try your hand at supporting details. Below is a main idea sentence. Write several detail sentences to support the main idea.

5.   Air has several unique properties. _____

_____

_____

_____

_____

_____

_____

_____

_____

_____

_____

Layers of Information

The Earth's atmosphere is divided into five layers. Each of these layers has its own properties. Use the diagram to help you record important information. Jot down words or phrases in each layer to help you remember details. An example has been done for you.

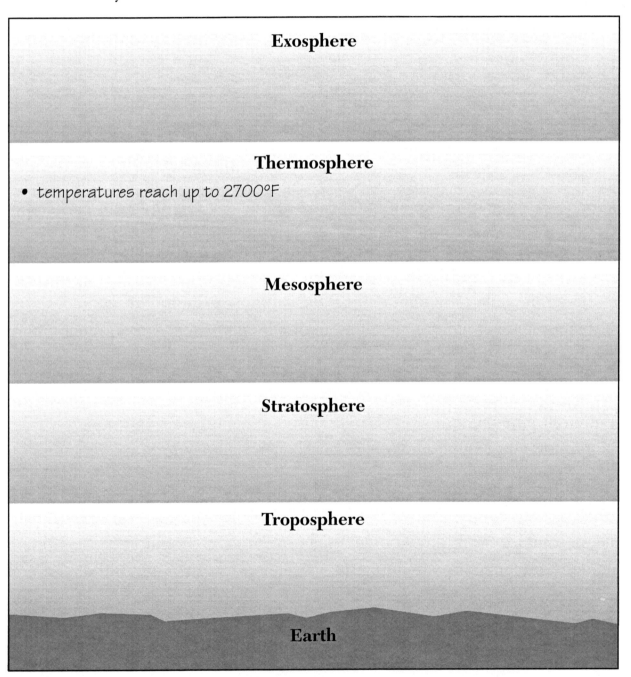

Exosphere

Thermosphere
- temperatures reach up to 2700°F

Mesosphere

Stratosphere

Troposphere

Earth

Name _____

Balloon Basics

Use balloons to learn about the basic properties of air. Try the first experiment to find out more about the weight of air. The second experiment will show you how temperature affects air.

Experiment 1

Materials
- ❏ 2 balloons of the same size and shape
- ❏ stick or dowel about a foot long
- ❏ string
- ❏ pin

Procedure
- Blow up both balloons to the same size. Use a short piece of string to tie one balloon to each end of the stick.

- Tie a piece of string about a foot long around the center of the stick. Hold the stick by the string. Adjust the position of the string so the stick balances straight across.

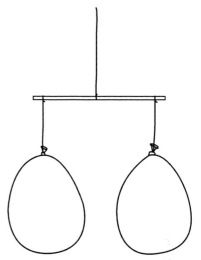

Stop and Predict

What will happen if I pop one of the balloons? _____

_____

- Now use the pin to pop one of the balloons. Observe what happens.

continued

Balloon Basics *continued*

Experiment 2

Materials
- ❏ 2 balloons of the same size and shape
- ❏ permanent marker
- ❏ small baking dish (just large enough to put a blown-up balloon in)
- ❏ refrigerator or cooler of ice
- ❏ oven or hair dryer

Procedure

- Blow up both balloons to the same size. Mark one with an H for hot and one with a C for cold.

- Put the H balloon in the baking dish. Place the dish in either a warm oven (heated to 200°F and then turned off) or blow on it with the hair dryer. Ask an adult to help you with the oven.

- Put the C balloon in the refrigerator or cooler.

Stop and Predict

What will happen to each of the balloons? _____

_____   _____

- After 10 minutes, compare the balloons.

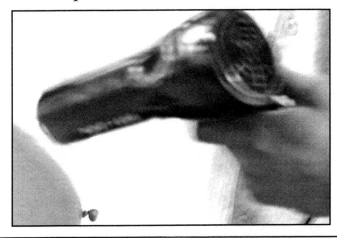

continued

©Perfection Learning®

Balloon Basics *continued*

Conclusions
Experiment 1
1. What happened when you popped the balloon?

_____

_____

_____

_____

2. What does this show you about air? Why?

_____

_____

_____

_____

Experiment 2
3. What happened to each balloon?

_____

_____

_____

_____

4. What does this show you about air?

_____

_____

_____

_____

Fifteen-Question Objective Test

Directions: Match each word and its definition.

_____ 1. atmosphere

_____ 2. molecule

_____ 3. water vapor

_____ 4. dense

_____ 5. anemometer

a. water in the form of a gas

b. having particles that are closer together and more tightly packed

c. mixture of gases that surrounds the Earth or any other body in space

d. instrument that measures wind speed

e. tiny particle of a substance made of two or more atoms

Directions: Answer each statement True (T) or False (F).

_____ 6. Air has weight and takes up space.

_____ 7. The molecules in air are packed together tightly.

_____ 8. Gravity pulls air molecules toward the center of the Earth.

_____ 9. A weather vane measures air pressure.

_____ 10. Wind is moving air.

Directions: Choose the best answer to complete each statement.

11. Which gas makes up the largest part of the Earth's atmosphere?

    a. oxygen

    b. carbon dioxide

    c. nitrogen

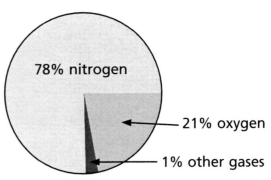

continued

Air and Wind
Fifteen-Question Objective Test continued

12. Mrs. Spencer's class did a science experiment. The students pushed a deflated balloon inside a clean 2-liter bottle. Then they stretched the mouth of the balloon over the mouth of the bottle. When the students tried to blow up the balloon, they couldn't. Why not?

    a. The bottle was made of plastic.

    b. The bottle was already filled with air.

    c. The balloon was too big for the bottle.

13. The layer of the atmosphere that we breathe and where most clouds and weather form is the

    a. troposphere.

    b. thermosphere.

    c. exosphere.

14. The area of the atmosphere that absorbs and scatters dangerous rays from the Sun is called the

    a. hot zone.

    b. sun screen.

    c. ozone layer.

15. The scale that classifies all winds according to their speed and strength is the

    a. WARP Scale.

    b. Beaufort Wind Scale.

    c. Barometric Scale.

Reading Essentials
in Science

Earth Movements
in Brief

The natural world changes every day. Planetary forces, underground movements, and wind and water currents all contribute to the changing Earth.

Evidence of the Earth's movement can be seen as seasons come and go and day turns to night. The Earth's revolution around the Sun on its tilted axis is responsible for the changing seasons. Locations near the equator and poles don't experience different seasons, though, because the Earth's tilt affects the amount of direct sunlight they receive. The Earth rotates on its axis once every 24 hours. As the Earth turns, the side of the Earth facing the Sun experiences day, while the side away from the Sun has night. Because the Earth's movement isn't felt, it took scientists centuries to prove that the planet does indeed move.

The Earth is divided into four layers—the inner and outer cores, the mantle, and the crust. Rocks cycle through these layers, changing the Earth's surface. This surface is broken into pieces called *tectonic plates*. The plates slowly move on the molten magma below. This action causes the Earth's crust to drift along the surface of the planet.

The movement of tectonic plates along with underground and aboveground forces creates mountains. When plates collide and the land buckles, fold mountains are formed. Large sections of rock that push up through cracks in plates become fault-block mountains. Magma that pushes against the Earth's crust results in dome mountains. The erosion of sedimentary rock above ground produces plateau mountains. When magma wells up between two separating plates, hardened lava builds up into volcanic mountains.

Weathering and erosion also result in tremendous changes in the Earth's surface. Physical weathering is the wearing away and breaking down of rocks and soil by wind, water, plants, and animals. Chemical weathering causes the minerals inside rock to change. This occurs when rain eats away at rock. After rocks are broken down through weathering processes, erosion moves the materials from one place to another. The main forces of erosion are wind, water, and ice.

Earth is always on the move. These movements continue to shape the planet and change the world.

Reading Exploration Essentials

Vocabulary

active	astronomer	cave
core	crust	current
erode	erosion	fault
groundwater	lava	magma
mantle	mineral	plate tectonics
revolution	rotation	sediment
tectonic plate	tide	weathering

Reading Exploration

prereading

Preview the cover and pictures in *Earth Movements*. Pair students and pose the question "What moves or changes on Earth?" Share responses.

during reading

Introduce the Question-Answer Relationship (QAR) strategy. Explain the three types of questions.

QAR Question Types

Right There—answers can be found directly in the text, usually within one sentence

Think and Search—answers combine several ideas from the book

Author and Me—answers connect a student's prior knowledge/experience with information in the book

Divide into teams and distribute copies (one per student) of questions for *Earth Movements*. A reproducible page of questions can be found on page 36. Students will need to record their answers on a separate sheet of paper. After each chapter, allow time for teams to meet and share answers they found. Remind students that the Author and Me questions may have different responses.

postreading

Assign each team several of the QAR questions for an after-reading discussion (the actual number will depend on the number of teams in your class). Ask each team to share its answers with the class.

continued

QAR Questions for *Earth Movements*

Right There

1. How long does it take for the Earth to rotate once?

2. What is the Earth's crust made of?

3. How much of the Earth's land is covered by mountains?

4. Where do most volcanic mountains begin?

5. How do animals cause weathering?

6. What are the three main forces of erosion?

Think and Search

1. Why was Nicolaus Copernicus considered the Father of Astronomy?

2. Why is the center of the Earth divided into two parts—the inner and outer cores?

3. How are plateau mountains different from the other types of mountains?

4. What is the difference between physical and chemical weathering?

Author and Me

1. Would you rather live near the equator, near the poles, or somewhere in between? Why?

2. On which tectonic plate do you live?

3. What type(s) of mountains can be found near your city or town?

4. What are some signs of weathering or erosion in your own environment?

Moving Magic Squares

Get moving and learn the vocabulary words from *Earth Movements*. Match each word with its meaning. Place the number of the word in the correct lettered box. Each row and column will add up to 18. One example has been done for you.

A. rise and fall of the ocean due to the Moon's gravity B. break in the Earth's crust due to stress C. to wear down and carry away pieces of rock, sand, or soil D. still erupts occasionally E. small pieces of rocks, minerals, and soil F. liquid rock above the Earth's surface G. outer layer of the Earth H. movement of one object around another I. study of the movement of the Earth's plates	2. fault 3. crust 4. lava 5. plate tectonics 6. ~~sediment~~ 7. tide 8. active 9. erode 10. revolution

A	B	C
D	**E** 6	**F**
G	**H**	**I**

continued

Name _____

Moving Magic Squares *continued*

A. process of breaking down rocks into smaller pieces B. center of the Earth C. movement of an object around a fixed point D. steady flow of water in a particular direction E. liquid rock within the Earth F. layer of the Earth between the crust and core G. movement of rock, sand, and soil by wind, water, or ice H. nonliving substance that makes up rock I. piece of the Earth's crust	2. core 3. tectonic plate 4. current 5. erosion 6. magma 7. rotation 8. mantle 9. weathering 10. mineral

A	B	C
D	E	F
G	H	I

Moving Opinions

A *fact* is a proven truth. An *opinion* is one person's feelings or ideas. Read the sentences below. Most of them are facts about the Earth's movement. But a few opinions moved in where they don't belong. Find these opinions and cross them out.

1. One revolution around the Sun takes about $365\frac{1}{4}$ days.

2. The Earth's revolution around the Sun causes the change of seasons.

3. The people who didn't believe Copernicus's ideas about the Earth were foolish.

4. The crust is the Earth's outer layer.

5. People should not live along faults in the Earth's crust.

6. The Sierra Nevada are fault-block mountains.

7. The Mid-Atlantic Ridge is the longest mountain range in the world.

8. Studying volcanoes is an exciting career.

9. Water is the main cause of chemical weathering.

10. Glaciers are slow-moving masses of ice.

◉ **One Step Further:** Choose one of the opinion sentences. Write a short paragraph supporting that opinion. Use facts from *Earth Movements*. If you don't agree with any of the opinions, then write a paragraph telling why you believe the opposite of one of the opinions.

Share your paragraph with a small group of classmates. Were they convinced of your opinion?

Mountains of Effects

Different forces cause different types of mountains. Fill in the cause of each type of mountain in the organizer below. Then give an example of each type of mountain. Refer to Chapter 4 of *Earth Movements* if necessary.

Cause	Effect	Example
	→ Fold Mountains →	
	→ Fault-Block Mountains →	
	→ Dome Mountains →	
	→ Plateau Mountains →	
	→ Volcanic Mountains →	

Name _____

A Downhill Journey

As a glacier moves downhill, it picks up rocks, sand, and soil. These materials (sediment) then travel with the chunk of ice. What happens to all of this sediment? Try the following experiment to find out.

Form a Hypothesis

What happens to sediment that's carried by a glacier?

The sediment carried by a glacier _____

_____.

Materials

- ❏ aluminum pie pan
- ❏ water
- ❏ freezer
- ❏ wooden board at least 3 feet long and 1 foot wide
- ❏ books
- ❏ baking sheet with sides
- ❏ soil and/or sand
- ❏ handful of pebbles

Procedure

- Fill the pie pan with water and freeze. Take the pie pan out of the freezer. Let it sit at room temperature until the top of the ice begins to melt.

- In the meantime, prop the board on a pile of books to make a slope. Start with a stack of books about a foot tall. Set the bottom of the board in the baking sheet. This will "catch" your glacier at the bottom of the slope.

- Sprinkle the soil, sand, and pebbles on the top half of the board. Leave the bottom half empty.

- Pop the ice out of the pie pan. Place your "glacier" at the top of your slope with the melting surface face down. Let the ice slide down the wood slowly. You may have to adjust the height of the slope to make the glacier move faster or slower. You want the ice to move at a slow, steady rate.

- Observe what happens to the sediment as the glacier makes its way down the slope. Let the rest of the glacier melt in the baking sheet. Watch what happens to the sediment.

continued

A Downhill Journey *continued*

Conclusions

1. What happened to the sediment as the glacier moved over it?

   _____

   _____

2. Was any sediment deposited on the lower slope?

   _____

   _____

3. Was any sediment carried all the way to the bottom of the slope (the baking sheet)? If so, how much?

   _____

   _____

4. What happened to the sediment in the baking sheet once all of the glacier melted?

   _____

   _____

5. Imagine the board was an actual mountain and the baking sheet was a river at the bottom of the mountain. What changes to the mountain and the river occurred as a result of the glacier's movement?

   _____

   _____

   _____

   _____

Name _____

Fifteen-Question Objective Test

Directions: Match each word and its definition.

_____ 1. revolution

_____ 2. fault

_____ 3. sediment

_____ 4. magma

_____ 5. plateau

a. break in the Earth's crust due to stress

b. flat area of land that is raised above surrounding land

c. movement of one object around another

d. small pieces of rocks, minerals, and soil

e. liquid rock within the Earth

Directions: Answer each statement True (T) or False (F).

_____ 6. The Earth's rotation on its axis causes day and night.

_____ 7. The Earth is one solid ball.

_____ 8. Volcanic mountains form when lava builds up along cracks in the Earth's crust.

_____ 9. Physical weathering causes the minerals inside a rock to change.

_____ 10. Water is the main cause of chemical weathering.

Directions: Choose the best answer to complete each statement.

11. The Earth's crust is broken into pieces called
    a. tectonic plates.
    b. mantles.
    c. continents.

continued

Earth Movements

Fifteen-Question Objective Test continued

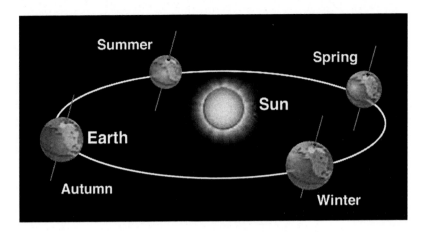

12. From this diagram you can tell that the
    a. Earth's revolution around the Sun causes the seasons.
    b. Earth's revolution around the Sun causes day and night.
    c. Sun's revolution around the Earth causes the seasons.

13. The three types of rock that cycle through the Earth are
    a. metamorphic, mineral, and tectonic.
    b. igneous, continental, and magma.
    c. sedimentary, metamorphic, and igneous.

14. When two tectonic plates push against each other until the land buckles up, they create
    a. plateau mountains.
    b. fault-block mountains.
    c. fold mountains.

15. Mike and his friends went on a nature hike at a nearby park. They saw several examples of erosion. What did they see?
    a. caves, canyons, and plateau mountains
    b. lakes, oceans, and glaciers
    c. earthquakes, volcanoes, and dome mountains

Soil Science
in Brief

All living things depend on soil. Soil is home to many organisms. It supports plant life, which in turn releases oxygen into the air and provides food for many animals. Soil also helps control and filter water.

There are five layers, or horizons, in the Earth's crust. The bottom layer is solid rock called *bedrock*. Above the bedrock lies weathered parent material. This layer consists of broken pieces of rock that have been weathered by wind or water. The subsoil is a mixture of broken rocks and organic material called *humus*. The topsoil contains a large amount of humus, making it a perfect home for plants and animals. Humans walk, live, and build on the ground level layer, which is often covered with leaves and other materials that will soon decompose and return to the soil.

Soil formation begins when rocks weather and break apart. Climate plays a major role in this weathering process. Wind, rain, ice, and temperature contribute to the breaking down of rocks. Organisms then make themselves at home in the weathered material. When these organisms die, they become part of the soil. This cycle continues until the soil is mature and fertile.

Soils are classified according to their mineral composition, grain size, and texture. Three main types of soil are sand, silt, and clay. Sand is mainly composed of large particles of quartz separated by big spaces. This makes sandy soil too "loose" to hold minerals and water for plants. The particles in silt are smaller and better able to hold water and nutrients. Silt is fairly light, however, and tends to blow away easily. Clay is very fine and sticky when wet. It is difficult for plants and animals to live in clay soil because of its tight spaces. Loam is a mixture of sand, silt, and clay. It is the perfect soil for many plants.

Soil scientists (pedologists) are always working to find better ways to keep soils healthy, prevent erosion, and improve farming practices. Solutions to erosion include planting trees in open areas, rotating grazing lands, and setting up windbreaks. Fertilizer use, no-till farming, crop rotation, and cover crop planting are productive farming practices. Keeping the soil healthy benefits all living things on Earth.

Reading Exploration Essentials

Vocabulary

bedrock	cast	decompose
decomposer	deforestation	erosion
fertile	horizon	humus
mineral	nutrient	organic matter
organism	subsoil	texture
topsoil	weathered	windbreak

Reading Exploration

prereading

Pose the following questions to the class: What is soil? What is dirt?

After individual think time, elicit responses and record them in a two-column chart on the board or overhead. Compare the ideas on both sides. Then read Chapter 1 of *Soil Science* together and combine the ideas into one definition of soil/dirt.

during reading

Copy made. Cut and glue in journal.

Before reading Chapter 2, present this anticipation guide. Make an overhead transparency for students to copy or hand out individual copies. Ask students to complete the "before reading" column. Encourage students to pair up and share their responses.

Before Reading Chapters 2–5 of *Soil Science* (agree or disagree)	Soil Statements	After Reading Chapters 2–5 of *Soil Science* (agree or disagree)
	The Earth's crust is divided into several layers.	
	Soil begins with rocks.	
	Earthworms are good for soil.	
	It takes a long time for healthy soil to form.	
	There is more than one type of soil.	
	Farming can both help and harm soil.	

postreading

Return to the anticipation guide and have students fill out the "after reading" column. Share responses in small groups or with the whole class.

Digging for Words

Read each sentence. Determine if the italicized word is a noun or a verb. Remember, a *noun* is a person, place, thing, or idea. A *verb* is an action word. Write N or V on the line behind each sentence. Then dig through the word search puzzle and find all the words.

1. Soil is home to millions of tiny *organisms*. _____

2. Soil holds the water and *minerals* that plants need to grow. _____

3. The layers of the Earth's crust are called *horizons*. _____

4. The bottom horizon is solid rock called *bedrock*. _____

5. Bedrock is *weathered* by wind or water, leaving behind a layer of broken rock pieces. _____

6. The *subsoil* is a mixture of rock particles and a small amount of organic matter. _____

7. The ground level layer is rich in *organic matter*. _____

8. *Topsoil* is perfect for sprouting seeds and growing roots. _____

9. Healthy soil is about 5 to 10 percent *humus*. _____

10. When living things in soil die, they *decompose* and return to the soil. _____

11. The *nutrients* in organic matter make soil good for plant life. _____

12. *Decomposers* are soil's best friends. _____

13. The nutrient-rich *casts* of earthworms make soil more fertile. _____

14. Soils can have different *textures* and particle sizes. _____

15. *Erosion* occurs when soil is moved from one location to another. _____

16. *Deforestation* and the overgrazing of cattle contribute to erosion. _____

17. *Windbreaks* block wind from reaching open areas of soil. _____

continued

Digging for Words *continued*

```
O  B  S  F  M  W  C  N  D  E  M  D  H  D  D
T  R  B  M  O  I  O  A  S  T  E  K  O  E  Q
L  K  G  W  S  I  N  O  S  C  J  T  R  F  D
I  I  Z  A  S  I  P  E  O  T  E  X  I  O  E
O  U  O  O  N  M  N  M  R  X  S  O  Z  R  R
S  U  R  S  O  I  P  A  T  A  M  I  O  E  E
P  E  G  C  B  O  C  U  G  W  L  Y  N  S  H
O  H  E  Z  S  U  R  M  G  R  L  S  S  T  T
T  D  X  E  T  E  S  I  A  H  O  T  T  A  A
G  B  R  T  S  W  U  Z  P  T  W  E  R  T  E
G  S  T  N  U  T  R  I  E  N  T  S  G  I  W
S  K  A  E  R  B  D  N  I  W  V  E  W  O  X
K  C  O  R  D  E  B  H  U  M  U  S  R  N  B
```

BEDROCK   CASTS   DECOMPOSE

DECOMPOSERS   DEFORESTATION   EROSION

HORIZONS   HUMUS   MINERALS

NUTRIENTS   ORGANIC MATTER   ORGANISMS

SUBSOIL   TEXTURES   TOPSOIL

WEATHERED   WINDBREAKS

A Grain of Difference

Soils are classified according to their unique characteristics. Sand, silt, and clay are three main types of soil. How are these soils alike and different? Read Chapter 4 of *Soil Science*. Use the chart below to record information about the three kinds of soil. Then answer the questions below.

Sand	Silt	Clay

1. Which soil has the largest grains? _____

2. Which soil has the least space between its particles? _____

3. Which of the three soils is best for growing plants? _____

Why? _____

_____

◎ **One Step Further:** Loam is the "perfect" soil. Write a recipe for making loam on an index card. Decorate your recipe card and give it to a gardener you know.

A Soil Story

Solid bedrock eventually turns into loose, crumbly topsoil. How does this happen? Review Chapter 3 of *Soil Science*. Then retell the story of soil formation from the point of view of the bedrock. Will you split apart when water freezes in your cracks? Will you become home to lichens or earthworms? What plants will grow in you when you've become mature soil?

Use the organizer to plan your story. Write a rough draft on a separate sheet of paper. Ask a partner to proofread your story. Then write your final copy.

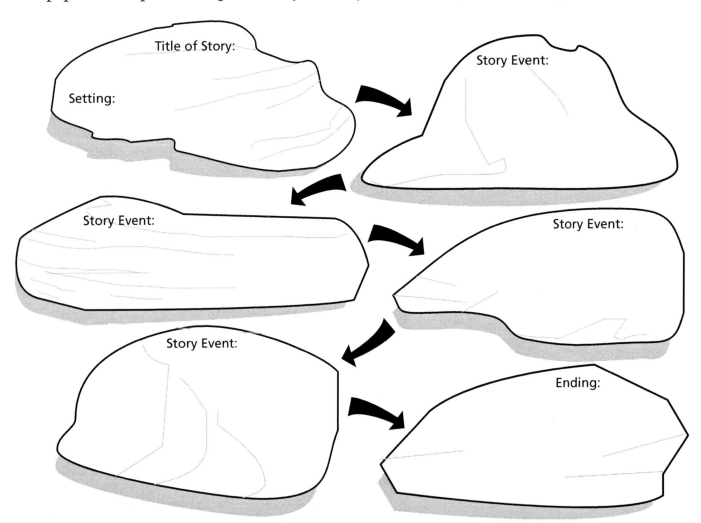

⊚ **One Step Further:** Illustrate several of the events in your story. Then share your illustrated story with your class.

Digging Up Dirt

You've learned all about soil. Now find out what kind of dirt lives in your own backyard.

Materials

- ❏ small patch of soil
  (get permission before you dig)
- ❏ plastic shovel or large spoon
- ❏ paper plate
- ❏ flashlight

> **Teacher Note:** For students without easy access to soil, provide a variety of soils for students to observe.

Procedure

- Use the shovel or spoon to dig down about a foot in the soil. Observe any changes in the soil as you dig deeper.

- Now scoop some soil onto the plate. Use the flashlight to examine the soil closely. Feel the soil. Make a sketch of your soil sample.

- Consider the following questions:

  – Are there any plant roots, fertilizers, or other materials in the soil?

  – Are the particles loose or tightly packed?

  – Does the soil feel gritty or smooth?

  – What color is the soil?

  – Are there any creatures crawling in the soil?

  – Can you identify the type of soil in your sample?

  – Would the soil be good for growing?

Conclusions

On a separate sheet of paper, write a paragraph describing your soil. Include the answers to the questions above. Add any other information you learned from your study. Attach your soil sketch to your paragraph.

Name _____

Directions: Match each word and its definition.

_____ 1. organism

_____ 2. weather

_____ 3. nutrient

_____ 4. subsoil

_____ 5. fertile

a. good for growing; rich in nutrients

b. material that plants and animals need to live and grow

c. layer of soil that's a mixture of rock particles and organic matter

d. to break down into smaller pieces

e. living thing

Directions: Answer each statement True (T) or False (F).

_____ 6. Soil absorbs water for plant and animal use.

_____ 7. The Earth's crust consists of several layers called *horizons*.

_____ 8. Topsoil is solid rock at the top of the Earth's crust.

_____ 9. Soil begins with rocks.

_____ 10. Farming can damage soil.

Directions: Choose the best answer to complete each statement.

11. Organic material that comes from the remains of plants or animals is called

   a. humus.

   b. subsoil.

   c. bedrock.

continued

©Perfection Learning®

Soil Science
Fifteen-Question Objective Test continued

12. Mushrooms and earthworms are

    a. decomposers.

    b. casts.

    c. weathered parent materials.

13. Jenni bought three pots of the same size. She filled one with sand, one with clay, and one with loam. Then she planted a bean seed in each pot. She watered all of the seeds with the same amount of water. Which plant most likely grew best?

    a. The plant in sand.

    b. The plant in loam.

    c. The plant in clay.

14. Soil erosion is the

    a. breaking down of plants and animals in the soil.

    b. disappearance of grazing lands.

    c. movement of soil by wind or water

15. Which layer of the Earth's crust is bedrock?

    a. 1

    b. 2

    c. 3

1

2

3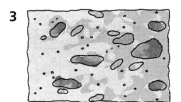

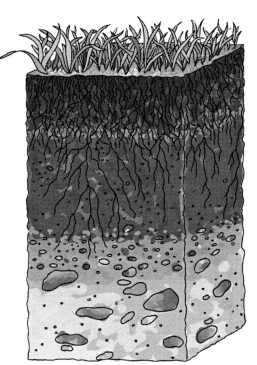

Water, Water, Everywhere
in Brief

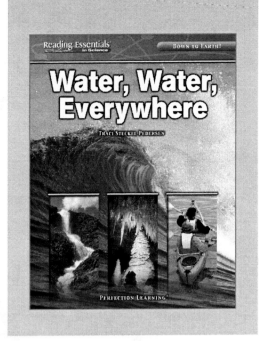

Water plays a major role on Earth. It moves in a constant cycle from the ground to the air and back again, affecting the weather, shaping the land, and nourishing all living things.

Each water molecule is made of two positively-charged hydrogen atoms and one negatively-charged oxygen atom. The attraction between these atoms is the reason water "sticks" together in drops and puddles.

Water is the only substance on Earth that naturally exists in three forms—liquid, solid, and gas. Only a tiny amount of all the water on Earth is available for human use. The rest is salt water in the oceans or freshwater locked in glaciers.

The three main processes that power the water cycle are evaporation, condensation, and precipitation. Evaporation takes place at all temperatures but occurs faster at higher temperatures. As water vapor cools, it condenses into liquid water. Clouds are a result of condensation at high altitudes.

When clouds get too full and heavy, the water falls to the ground as rain, snow, or ice. This is known as precipitation. When precipitation reaches the Earth, most of it lands in the oceans or other bodies of water. The rest becomes groundwater or runoff.

Water is known as the universal solvent because it has the ability to dissolve more substances than any other liquid on Earth. Water is a main force of both weathering and erosion.

Throughout history, humans have worked hard to control water for their own purposes. Early cultures built irrigation systems. Then dams and levees were constructed to contain floodwaters. Water treatment plants take water from its source and purify it so it can be distributed throughout a community. Sewage treatment plants clean water that has been used by people and then return it to its original source. Human efforts along with the natural water cycle ensure that water really is everywhere it needs to be.

Reading Exploration Essentials

Vocabulary

aqueduct	atom	condensation
dehydrated	dense	deposited
dissolve	erosion	evaporation
groundwater	molecule	precipitation
reservoir	runoff	surface water
transpiration	volume	water vapor
weathering	well	

Reading Exploration

prereading

Ask students to work in small groups to list ways in which they use water. When they've finished, invite them to preview *Water, Water, Everywhere* by skimming the table of contents, headings, and pictures. Then ask them to add any ideas to their original lists. Compile a class list of ways people use water. Post the list in the classroom or create a bulletin board by writing each way on a water drop and adding the heading "Water, Water, Everywhere."

during reading

As students read the book, encourage them to add ways that people use water to the list or bulletin board (supply extra water drops for students).

postreading

Conclude the discussion on ways people use water by allowing students to share ideas they added to the list or board. Elicit student reactions to all of the ways they use water. Were they surprised at how important water is to them?

Ask students to create a diagram of the water cycle that could replace/enhance the one in Chapter 3 of the book. Diagrams should include the basic steps in the cycle as well as additional details. For example, students could add information about (or pictures of) the different types of precipitation or draw the paths water can take when it hits the ground. Display the new diagrams in the classroom.

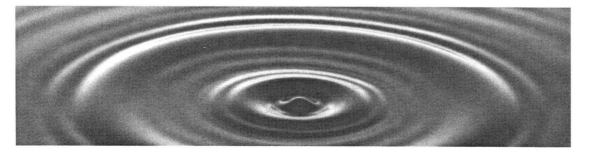

Watery Words

Don't drown in the vocabulary words from *Water, Water, Everywhere*. Learn the words by completing the following activities. Use the book glossary or a dictionary if you need help.

● Several of the words were made by adding an ending to a base word. Write the base word on the line.

1. dehydrated _____

2. transpiration _____

3. weathering _____

4. erosion _____

5. condensation _____

6. deposited _____

7. evaporation _____

8. precipitation _____

● Now read the following sentences. Add an ending to the base word in parentheses to make the word fit in the sentence. Write the new word on the line.

9. The Romans built _____ to carry water into cities. (aqueduct)

10. Much of the water on Earth carries _____ minerals and chemicals in it. (dissolve)

11. Liquid water is _____ than ice. (dense)

12. Each water molecule is made of two hydrogen _____ and one oxygen atom bonded together. (atom)

continued

Name _____

Watery Words *continued*

⬤ Four of the vocabulary words are compound words. Two of these words are closed compounds (one word made of two words put together). The other two are open compounds (two separate words that go together to represent one idea). Write each of the words in a sentence that shows their meaning.

13. groundwater: _____

_____

14. runoff: _____

_____

15. surface water: _____

_____

16. water vapor: _____

_____

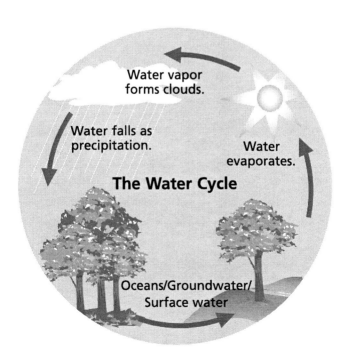

Water vapor forms clouds.

Water falls as precipitation.

Water evaporates.

The Water Cycle

Oceans/Groundwater/ Surface water

Name _____

Filtering Out Bad Facts

A water treatment plant takes water from its source and cleans it. This process includes adding chemicals and filtering out dirt particles. Now it's your turn! Get ready to filter out the bad facts below. Read each statement. Decide if it's correct or not. Cross out the incorrect statements.

1. A water molecule is made of two hydrogen atoms and one oxygen atom.

2. Water vapor is a liquid.

3. Steam is gaseous water that results from boiling.

4. Water covers about half of the Earth's surface.

5. When liquid water turns into a vapor, it's called precipitation.

6. Clouds are formed from condensation.

7. Rain that seeps into the ground becomes groundwater.

8. The Greeks created aqueducts for irrigation.

9. Reservoirs are barriers that hold back floodwaters.

10. Wastewater is cleaned by sewage treatment plants.

◉ **One Step Further:** Change a word or words in the incorrect statements to make them correct. Rewrite the new statements on the lines below.

_____

_____

_____

_____

_____

What I Think About Water

What are your thoughts about the information you learned in *Water, Water, Everywhere*? Fill in the chart on the next page to organize your ideas. Read each statement in the left-hand column. Then write your response to the information in the right-hand column. These responses may be reactions such as surprise, you already knew that, how it affects you, etc. You can also add extra information that you already knew that relates to the idea. You might also write down questions you have.

Then choose two more statements from the book that interest you. Write them in the "What the Author Says" column. Record the page numbers where the statements were found. Then write your responses to the information.

◉ **One Step Further:** Choose one of your thoughts from the chart. Write a short paragraph explaining what you think and why. Share your ideas with the class.

continued

Name _____

What I Think About Water *continued*

What the Author Says	Page Number	What I Think About It
The force of attraction between water molecules is why water sticks together.	7	
Water in a gas form surrounds you all the time.	9	
Only a very small amount of water on Earth is useful to you.	11	
The water that flows out of your faucet has traveled the world throughout time.	12	
Throughout history, humans have worked hard to control water for their own purposes.	19	

©Perfection Learning®

Name _____

A Disappearing Act

Evaporation plays an important role in the water cycle. It's responsible for moving water from the ground to the sky. Evaporation occurs at all temperatures. But is the rate of evaporation the same at all temperatures? Try this experiment to find out.

Materials
- ❏ 2 glass (or clear plastic) measuring cups with ounce markings
- ❏ water
- ❏ 2 indoor/outdoor thermometers

Procedure
- Fill both measuring cups to the 8-oz. mark.
- Find one warm location and one cold location. Warm locations could include outside in the Sun or inside near a heating vent. Cold locations could include outside on a cold day or inside an air-conditioned room. Place one cup in each location.
- Lay a thermometer near each of the cups. At 12:00 p.m. (noon), record the temperature near each cup. Also note how much water is in the cup. Repeat this procedure for 5 days.

Stop and Predict

From which cup will the most water evaporate? _____

_____

	Day 1	Day 2	Day 3	Day 4	Day 5
Temperature/ Amount of water in "warm" cup					
Temperature/ Amount of water in "cold" cup					

continued

©Perfection Learning®

Name _____

Water, Water, Everywhere

A Disappearing Act *continued*

Conclusions

1. What was the temperature difference between the two locations each day?

   Day 1: _____

   Day 2: _____

   Day 3: _____

   Day 4: _____

   Day 5: _____

2. What was the total amount of water that evaporated from each cup?

   Warm Cup: _____

   Cold Cup: _____

3. From which cup did the most water evaporate? _____

   Why do you think that is? _____

   _____

4. Does heat affect the rate of evaporation? _____

   If so, in what way? _____

   _____

5. Imagine you hung a load of wet laundry in both of your experiment locations.

   In which place would the clothes dry faster? _____

   Why? _____

   _____

©Perfection Learning®

**62 Conducting a Science Experiment, Predicting Outcomes, Reading and Using a Chart,
   Analyzing Information, Drawing Conclusions, Making Inferences**

Fifteen-Question Objective Test

Directions: Match each word and its definition.

_____ 1. weathering   a. left behind or dropped off

_____ 2. aqueduct   b. natural process of breaking rocks down into smaller pieces

_____ 3. deposited   c. area where water is stored

_____ 4. reservoir   d. process of water changing from a gas to a liquid

_____ 5. condensation   e. pipe or channel for moving water

Directions: Answer each statement True (T) or False (F).

_____ 6. Vapor is water in solid form.

_____ 7. Humidity is the amount of water vapor in the air.

_____ 8. Most of the water on Earth is freshwater.

_____ 9. Water is a main force of erosion.

_____ 10. Levees and dams are built to control flooding.

Directions: Choose the best answer to complete each statement.

11. Clouds are formed from

     a. transpiration.

     b. condensation.

     c. oxidation.

continued

Water, Water, Everywhere

Fifteen-Question Objective Test continued

12. From this diagram, you can tell that water
    a. is made of two hydrogen atoms and one oxygen atom.
    b. is the only natural substance that exists in three forms.
    c. dissolves more substances than any other liquid.

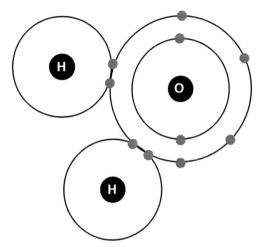

13. When water falls from the sky to the ground, it's called
    a. evaporation.
    b. irrigation.
    c. precipitation.

14. Rain or snow that soaks into the ground is called
    a. surface water.
    b. runoff.
    c. groundwater.

15. Chris left a glass of water outside on a hot, sunny day. When he returned, the glass was still standing, but most of the water was gone. Where did it most likely go?
    a. It dripped out the bottom of the glass.
    b. It evaporated into the air.
    c. It splashed out of the glass.

Reading Essentials
in Science

What's Up with the Weather?
A Look at Climate
in Brief

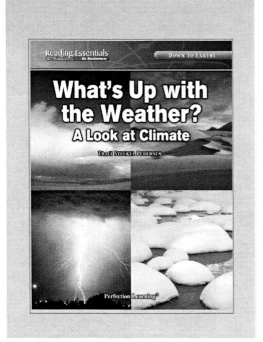

Climate is the normal weather in an area over time. It includes temperatures, precipitation, winds, sunlight, and humidity.

The main factors that affect a region's climate are sunlight, wind, ocean currents, and geographic features. An area's latitude determines how much direct sunlight it receives. The land at the equator receives the most direct sunlight, making it warmer. The farther you move away from the tropics, the less direct sunlight the Earth receives, so the climate is cooler. Global winds and ocean currents move air and water from one location to another, affecting climates. Since water cools down and heats up more slowly than land, coastal areas have smaller differences between their winter and summer temperatures. Temperature also changes with altitude. Mountainous areas are much cooler than flat areas at the same latitude. Mountains can also block wind and precipitation, causing one side to get a lot of rain while the other side is a dry desert.

The climates of the world can be divided into groups. The warmer climates are the tropical wet, tropical wet and dry, subtropical moist, subtropical dry summer, dry (semiarid), and desert climates. The oceanic moist, continental moist, highland, subarctic, and ice cap climates are cooler climates. Each of these climates is summarized.

Normally climates are steady and predictable. However, a few unusual climate events and changes have occurred throughout time. From the 1350s to the 1850s, a cold spell known as the Little Ice Age hit parts of the world. Scientists believe the cold may have been due to a decrease in the Sun's activity and/or an increase in volcanic activity.

Hundreds of years ago, fishermen noticed the effects of El Niño. During El Niño, warmer water temperatures in the Pacific Ocean add heat and moisture to the air. These changes bring weather that temporarily differs from normal. This phenomenon still occurs today.

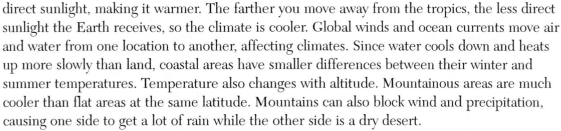

Over the past 100 years, the atmosphere seems to be trapping more heat than usual, causing an overall temperature increase of 1°F. Some scientists believe this is because people are releasing more heat-trapping gases such as carbon dioxide into the atmosphere. This warming of the atmosphere by human actions is known as the greenhouse effect. Many people are taking actions to stop global warming. Reducing the burning of greenhouse gases, recycling garbage, and planting trees are steps that may help prevent harmful changes to climates around the world.

Reading Exploration Essentials

Vocabulary		
climate	current	deciduous
drought	equator	evaporating
global warming	habitat	hemisphere
humidity	latitude	monsoon
plateau	pole	precipitation
steppe	tropics	tundra
wind		

Reading Exploration

prereading

Divide the class into three groups. Tell each group that they've just won a trip to one of the following locations: the Amazon Rain Forest, the Sahara Desert, or the North Pole. Point out each of these destinations on a globe.

Ask each group to decide on five items they will pack for their trip based on where they're going. Remind them to focus on objects such as clothing, recreational items, etc., that would be determined by the climate.

Have groups share their items and explain why they chose them. Guide them toward reasons that have to do with weather/climate (temperatures, precipitation, terrain, etc.). Develop the idea that their choices were based on the climate of their destination.

during reading

Before reading each chapter, give each student one sticky note. Instruct students to mark one important fact from the chapter that they want to remember. Also make a stack of sticky notes available for students to mark any passages that they have questions about. Tell them to mark those notes with a question mark.

After each chapter, work in small groups to share important facts and answer questions.

postreading

Based on the information in the book, determine which world climate you and your students live in. What does this mean in terms of the weather patterns, seasons, land features, etc., in your community? Use the information to make a class poster or mural describing the climate in your community. Post your finished product in the hallway or lunchroom to share with other students.

Encourage students to bring in local or global current events that relate to weather and climate. Post them on a bulletin board and allow time for sharing.

Name _____

What's Up with the Weather? A Look at Climate

Climate Synonyms and Antonyms

A *synonym* is a word that means nearly the same as another word. *Chilly* is a synonym of *cold*. An *antonym* is a word that means nearly the opposite of another word. *Hot* is an antonym of *cold*.

Read each sentence below. Decide which word is a synonym of the italicized word. Write the correct letter on the line.

_____ 1. The warm, wet air from over the ocean provides constant *moisture* in subtropical moist climates.

_____ 2. The land in dry climates is often covered by *grasslands*.

_____ 3. Areas in the middle of each *half* of the Earth usually have changing seasons.

_____ 4. By the time air has crossed a mountain, most of the *rain* has fallen.

_____ 5. Climates create different types of *homes* for plants and animals.

a. hemisphere

b. humidity

c. precipitation

d. habitats

e. steppes

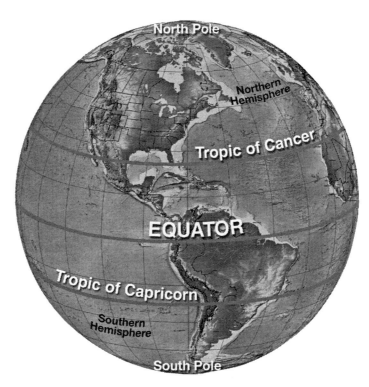

continued

Name _____

What's Up with the Weather? A Look at Climate

Climate Synonyms and Antonyms *continued*

Now decide which word is an antonym of the italicized word. Write the correct letter on the line.

_____ 1. Monsoons bring heavy rains that can cause terrible *flooding*.

_____ 2. Global *cooling* may cause glaciers to melt.

_____ 3. The highland climate is found in high mountains and *valleys*.

_____ 4. The equator is an imaginary line of *longitude* in the middle of the globe.

_____ 5. Cold temperatures in the polar climate keep water from *condensing*.

a. latitude

b. plateaus

c. evaporating

d. warming

e. drought

◉ **One Step Further:** Review the 12 climates from Chapters 3 and 4 of *What's Up with the Weather?* Can you find two climates that are nearly the opposite of each other?

_____   _____

Now choose one climate. Think of a new name for the climate that means nearly the same as the original name. Write the climate and its new name.

_____   _____

Name _____

What's Up with the Weather? A Look at Climate

A Warm Greeting

Global warming could result in many problems on Earth. Reread the section on global warming in Chapter 5 of *What's Up with the Weather?* Then write a letter to a friend or relative describing the problem and its possible effects. Explain what he or she can do to be part of the solution.

Dear _____,

_____

_____

_____

_____

_____

_____

_____

_____

_____

_____

_____

_____

Sincerely,

_____

©Perfection Learning®

Name _____

Content-Area Reading Strategies: Visualizing,
Monitoring, Making Connections

**What's Up with the Weather?
A Look at Climate**

Mapping My Climates

Think about how climate affects your life. Perhaps you live in an oceanic moist climate with mild seasons. Maybe you've taken a cruise to Hawaii or Alaska. You might even dream of someday climbing a mountain or going on a rain forest safari.

Choose five of the climates discussed in Chapters 3 and 4 of *What's Up with the Weather? A Look at Climate*. Your choices could include the climate where you live, a climate you've vacationed in, or a climate you someday hope to visit. Or you might just choose climates that interest you.

Follow the directions below to create your own climate map on the next page.

➤ Use five different colors to mark your climates on the map.
   (Refer to the map on page 10 of the book.)

➤ Draw in and label the equator, Tropic of Capricorn, and Tropic of Cancer.

➤ Label the North and South Poles.

➤ Label the oceans and continents.

➤ Add a compass rose.

➤ Make a map key.

◎ **One Step Further:** Identify any other locations that are important to your climate map. For example, label where you live, where you've vacationed, or where you hope to go someday.

continued

Name _____

What's Up with the Weather? A Look at Climate

Mapping My Climates *continued*

Name _____

Water Versus Land

Ocean beaches make great vacation spots. Why do places near an ocean have milder summers and winters? Try this experiment to find out.

Materials

- ❏ 2 clear plastic cups
- ❏ 1 cup of water
- ❏ 1 cup of soil
- ❏ 2 thermometers

> **Teacher Note:** This experiment is best done on a warm, sunny day.

Procedure

- Fill one cup with water and the other cup with soil. Let the cups sit at room temperature for at least 30 minutes.

- Put both cups outside in the Sun. After 15 minutes, take the temperature of the soil and water in each cup. Record the temperatures in the chart. Let the cups sit in the Sun for another 15 minutes. Record their temperatures.

- Now bring the cups back inside. Take the temperature of the soil and water after 15 minutes and after 30 minutes. Record the temperatures in the chart.

	Temperature after 15 minutes in the Sun	Temperature after 30 minutes in the Sun	Temperature after 15 minutes inside	Temperature after 30 minutes inside
Soil				
Water				

continued

©Perfection Learning®

Name _____

What's Up with the Weather? A Look at Climate

Water Versus Land *continued*

Conclusions

1. Did the soil or water heat up more quickly?

   _____

   _____

2. What was the difference in temperature between the soil and water after 30 minutes in the Sun?

   _____

   _____

3. Did the soil or water cool down more quickly?

   _____

   _____

4. Was there still a difference in temperature between the soil and water after 30 minutes inside? If so, what was the difference?

   _____

   _____

5. What does this experiment show you about the climate near an ocean?

   _____

   _____

   _____

Name _____

Fifteen-Question Objective Test

Directions: Match each word and its definition.

_____ 1. equator

_____ 2. hemisphere

_____ 3. humidity

_____ 4. precipitation

_____ 5. wind

a. half of the Earth

b. moving air

c. imaginary line running around the middle of the Earth

d. moisture that falls to the ground as rain, snow, hail, etc.

e. amount of moisture in the air

Directions: Answer each statement True (T) or False (F).

_____ 6. The climate in an area changes frequently.

_____ 7. Global winds carry warm air away from the equator and cold air away from the poles.

_____ 8. Water cools down and heats up more slowly than land.

_____ 9. The climate on one side of a mountain may be different from the climate on the other side.

_____ 10. The weather in one part of the world does not affect the weather in another part of the world.

Directions: Choose the best answer to complete each statement.

11. The climate in an area is determined by its
    a. plants, animals, and people.
    b. homes, businesses, and cities.
    c. temperatures, moisture, and winds.

continued

What's Up with the Weather? A Look at Climate

Fifteen-Question Objective Test continued

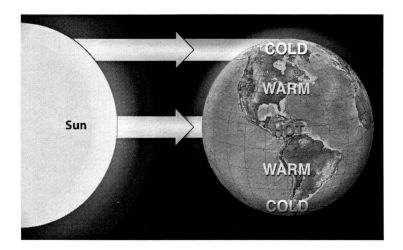

12. From this illustration, you can tell that the

    a. North and South Poles receive the most direct sunlight.

    b. land at the equator receives the most direct sunlight.

    c. tropics don't receive much direct sunlight.

13. Last summer, Traci went on a safari in a tropical wet climate. This summer, she went to a beach resort in an oceanic moist climate. What do her two vacation spots have in common?

    a. Both places receive a steady amount of rain.

    b. Both climates are found on all of the continents.

    c. Both climates have extremely hot temperatures year-round.

14. From the 1350s to the 1850s, parts of the world experienced a cold spell called the

    a. Long Cold Spell.

    b. Little Ice Age.

    c. Freezing Years.

15. The warming of the atmosphere is called the

    a. warming wave.

    b. global effect.

    c. greenhouse effect.

Answer Key

Air and Wind

Windy Words (page 24)
1. atmosphere; 2. troposphere; 3. water vapor; 4. global; 5. stratosphere; 6. ozone layer;
7. mesosphere; 8. thermosphere; 9. exosphere; 10. dense; 11. molecules; 12. gravity;
13. satellites

Get the Idea? (page 26)
1. Hot-air balloons work using the movement of hot and cold air. 2. The Sun and air are perfect partners in the creation of wind. 3. Several scales are used to classify winds. 4. Responses will vary but should resemble the following: Many tools are used to measure the properties of air and wind.
5. Responses will vary.

Layers of Information (page 28)
Responses will vary.

Balloon Basics (page 29)
1. The balance tipped so the popped balloon was higher than the inflated one. 2. This shows that air has weight since the balloon containing air weighed more than the empty one. 3. The hot balloon expanded, while the cold balloon shrunk. 4. This shows that heat makes air expand and cold makes air contract.

Fifteen-Question Objective Test (page 32)
1. c; 2. e; 3. a; 4. b; 5. d; 6. T; 7. F; 8. T; 9. F; 10. T; 11. c; 12. b; 13. a; 14. c; 15. b

Earth Movements

Moving Magic Squares (page 37)

A 7	B 2	C 9
D 8	E 6	F 4
G 3	H 10	I 5

A 9	B 2	C 7
D 4	E 6	F 8
G 5	H 10	I 3

Moving Opinions (page 39)
Students should cross out 3, 5, and 8.

continued

Mountains of Effects (page 40)

Cause	Effect	Possible Examples
Two tectonic plates push against each other, and the land buckles up and folds over.	Fold Mountains	Himalayan Mountains or Appalachian Mountains
Large sections of solid rock push up through a fault.	Fault-Block Mountains	Sierra Nevada
Magma hardens and pushes against the Earth's crust.	Dome Mountains	Black Hills
Rivers or glaciers wear down stacks of sedimentary rock.	Plateau Mountains	Catskill Mountains
Magma wells up through rifts and reaches the surface. Cooled lava builds up into mountains.	Volcanic Mountains	Mid-Atlantic Ridge or Hawaiian Islands

A Downhill Journey (page 41)
1. Responses will vary, but the glacier should pick up some of the soil, sand, and pebbles.
2. Responses will vary, but some of the sediment will most likely be deposited along the lower slope.
3. Responses will vary, but some of the sediment will most likely be carried all the way to the bottom of the slope. 4. Responses will vary, but any sediment will settle on the bottom of the baking sheet when all of the glacier has melted. 5. Responses will vary, but the soil at the top of the mountain will lose much of the minerals that it needs while the land at the bottom will be enriched by the sediment left behind by the glacier. The riverbed would be enriched by the sediment deposited there.

Fifteen-Question Objective Test (page 43)
1. c; 2. a; 3. d; 4. e; 5. b; 6. T; 7. F; 8. T; 9. F; 10. T; 11. a; 12. a; 13. c; 14. c; 15. a

continued

Soil Science

Digging for Words (page 47)
1. N; 2. N; 3. N; 4. N; 5. V; 6. N; 7. N; 8. N; 9. N; 10. V; 11. N; 12. N; 13. N; 14. N; 15. N; 16. N; 17. N

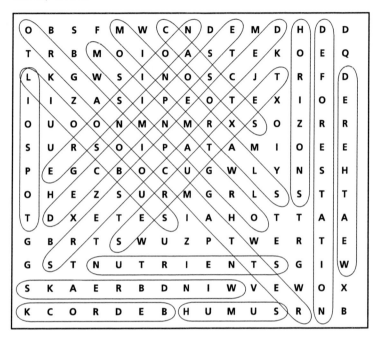

A Grain of Difference (page 49)
1. sand; 2. clay; 3. Silt is the best soil for growing plants because it is able to hold water and nutrients.

A Soil Story (page 50)
Responses will vary.

Digging Up Dirt (page 51)
Responses will vary.

Fifteen-Question Objective Test (page 52)
1. e; 2. d; 3. b; 4. c; 5. a; 6. T; 7. T; 8. F; 9. T; 10. T; 11. a; 12. a; 13. b; 14. c; 15. c

Water, Water, Everywhere

Watery Words (page 56)
1. dehydrate; 2. transpire; 3. weather; 4. erode; 5. condense; 6. deposit; 7. evaporate; 8. precipitate; 9. aqueducts; 10. dissolved; 11. denser; 12. atoms; 13–16. Responses will vary.

continued

Filtering Out Bad Facts (page 58)
Numbers 2, 4, 5, 8, and 9 should be crossed out.

One Step Further: Corrected statements should read as follows: 2. Water vapor is a gas. 4. Water covers about 70 percent of the Earth's surface. 5. When liquid water turns into a vapor, it's called evaporation. 8. The Romans created aqueducts for irrigation. 9. Dams are barriers that hold back floodwaters.

What I Think About Water (page 59)
Responses will vary.

A Disappearing Act (page 61)
1. Responses will vary. 2. Responses will vary. 3. Responses will vary, but the most water should evaporate from the cup in the warm location because the extra heat will help water molecules move faster so they can break free from their bonds and escape into the air. 4. Responses will vary, but the warmer the temperature, the faster evaporation takes place. 5. Responses will vary, but the clothes in the warm location will dry faster because the heat will speed up the evaporation of water from the clothes.

Fifteen-Question Objective Test (page 63)
1. b; 2. e; 3. a; 4. c; 5. d; 6. F; 7. T; 8. F; 9. T; 10. T; 11. b; 12. a; 13. c; 14. c; 15. b

What's Up with the Weather? A Look at Climate

Climate Synonyms and Antonyms (page 67)
1. b; 2. e; 3. a; 4. c; 5. d
1. e; 2. d; 3. b; 4. a; 5. c

A Warm Greeting (page 69)
Responses will vary.

Mapping My Climates (page 70)
Responses will vary.

Water Versus Land (page 72)
1. The soil should heat up more quickly. 2. Responses will vary. 3. The soil should cool down more quickly. 4. Responses will vary. 5. The experiment shows that water heats up and cools down more slowly than land. This is why temperatures near an ocean are cooler in the summer and warmer in the winter than temperatures on land at the same latitude.

Fifteen-Question Objective Test (page 74)
1. c; 2. a; 3. e; 4. d; 5. b; 6. F; 7. T; 8. T; 9. T; 10. F; 11. c; 12. b; 13. a; 14. b; 15. c